Disney · PIXAR

FINDING NEMO

TED SMART

At the edge of Australia's Great Barrier Reef, a terrible tragedy had befallen a clownfish named Marlin. One moment he'd been happily setting up home with his wife and their hundreds of eggs. The next moment, a barracuda attacked!

With a single swipe of its tail the big fish had knocked Marlin out cold. When he awoke, all that was left of his family was a single, damaged egg.

"It's okay," he said soothingly to the egg. "Daddy's here. I promise I will never let anything happen to you . . . Nemo."

It was a promise Marlin was determined to keep. He became very protective of Nemo, especially since he was born with one fin smaller than the other.

But Nemo didn't let anything hold him back. He was always full of fun, and couldn't wait to start school. Marlin, however, didn't really want him to go. He worried that something dreadful would happen.

"What's the one thing we have to remember about the ocean?" he reminded Nemo as they prepared to leave for school.

"It's not safe," Nemo sighed.

It was the first day of school, and Nemo was very excited. He couldn't wait to go and play with all the big kids. But Marlin wanted him to play on the sponge beds where the babies bounced. He thought it would be much safer.

Finally, Marlin reluctantly escorted Nemo over to Mr Ray, who was taking the class off to explore. "Don't worry," the teacher assured him. "We're going to stay together as a group."

Mr Ray took the kids right to where the reef gave way to the open ocean. Nemo and his new friends – Tad, Sheldon and Pearl – swam off to look at a white boat anchored overhead.

The kids dared each other to swim up to the boat and touch it. "Come on, Nemo," said Tad.

Just then, Marlin appeared, checking up on his son. He panicked because he thought Nemo was going to swim out into the open water. "You think you can do these things, but you just can't, Nemo!" he yelled.

Nemo was tired of his dad thinking he was too small and weak to do anything for himself, and was desperate to prove him wrong. As his concerned father called out to him, Nemo set off into the blue towards the boat. Soon the safety of the reef and all that he knew was far, far behind him.

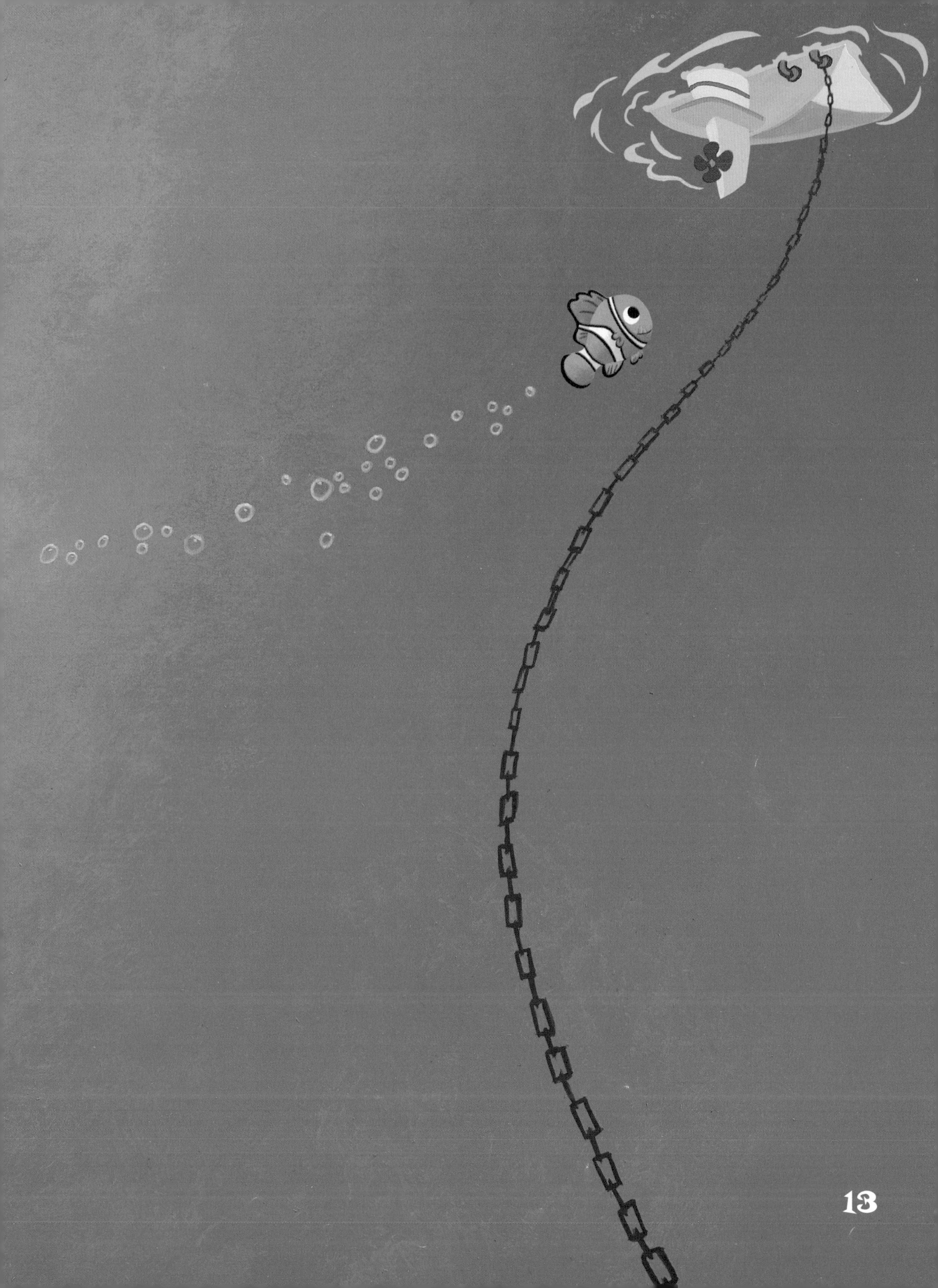

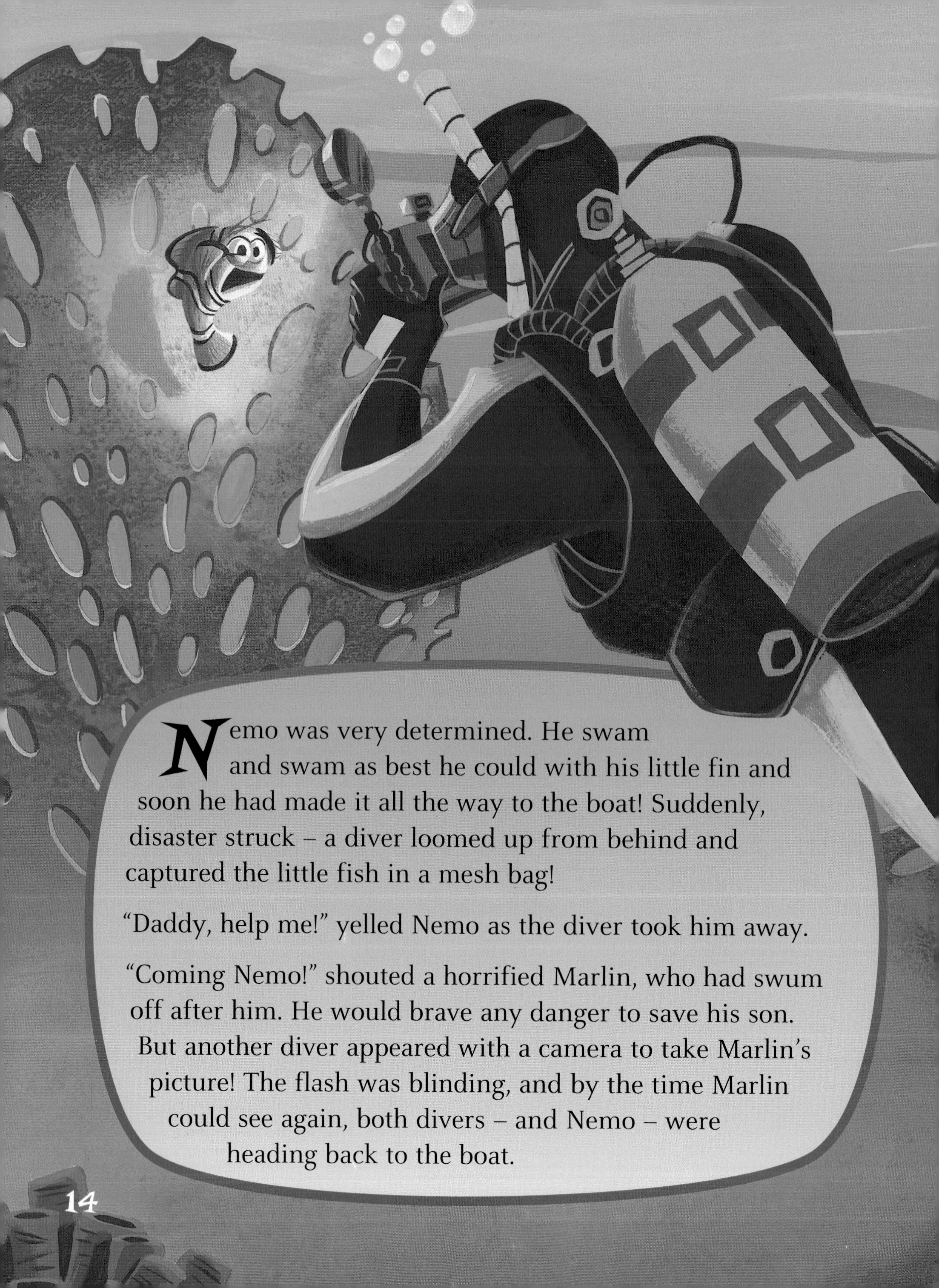

Nemo was very determined. He swam and swam as best he could with his little fin and soon he had made it all the way to the boat! Suddenly, disaster struck – a diver loomed up from behind and captured the little fish in a mesh bag!

"Daddy, help me!" yelled Nemo as the diver took him away.

"Coming Nemo!" shouted a horrified Marlin, who had swum off after him. He would brave any danger to save his son. But another diver appeared with a camera to take Marlin's picture! The flash was blinding, and by the time Marlin could see again, both divers – and Nemo – were heading back to the boat.

Marlin swam after the divers as fast as he could, but he just couldn't catch up. In a matter of moments, they had climbed back on board their boat.

The engine started, and the power of the propellers pushed Marlin backwards. Then the boat sped away, so quickly that one diver lost his balance and dropped his mask overboard. Before long, the boat had vanished over the horizon.

"It can't be gone!" cried Marlin in despair. "Nemo, no!"

Suddenly he was all alone.

Marlin swam around, desperately asking every fish he met if they'd seen a white boat pass by, but they were too busy or too unfriendly to help.

Only Dory, a kind blue tang fish, had seen a boat and offered to help, but unfortunately, she had a little problem.

"I forget things almost instantly," she explained. "It runs in my family . . . at least I think it does . . . uh, where are they?" Dory looked around, puzzled. She couldn't even remember meeting Marlin! "Can I help you?" she asked politely.

Marlin was baffled by Dory's behaviour. But before he could make his excuses and swim off to search for Nemo elsewhere, a great white shark named Bruce appeared! He insisted the two fish come with him to a little get-together he was having.

"I love parties!" said Dory excitedly. "That sounds like fun!"

To Marlin, it sounded more like a trap – but when Bruce placed his fins tightly round the two of them he knew there was no escape. They were taken to a sunken submarine to meet Bruce's friends. But this was no party.

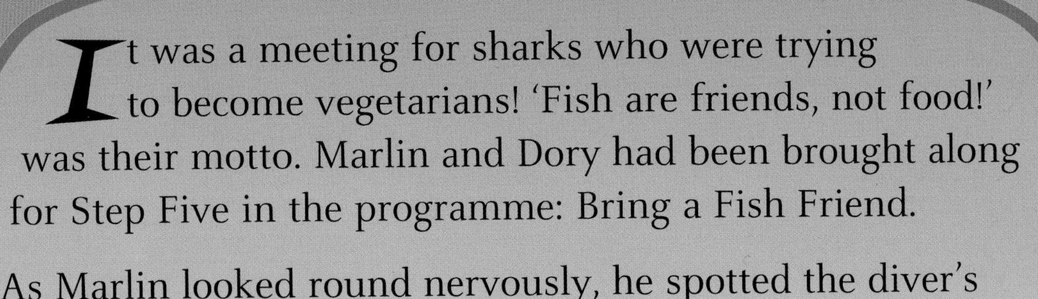

It was a meeting for sharks who were trying to become vegetarians! 'Fish are friends, not food!' was their motto. Marlin and Dory had been brought along for Step Five in the programme: Bring a Fish Friend.

As Marlin looked round nervously, he spotted the diver's mask that had fallen off the boat! There were markings on the mask – what did they mean?

Dory thought they should show the mask to the sharks, but Marlin wanted to leave.

They had a bit of a struggle over the mask, and the strap pinged against Dory's nose! It drew a tiny trickle of blood – which sent Bruce wild!

HERMAN

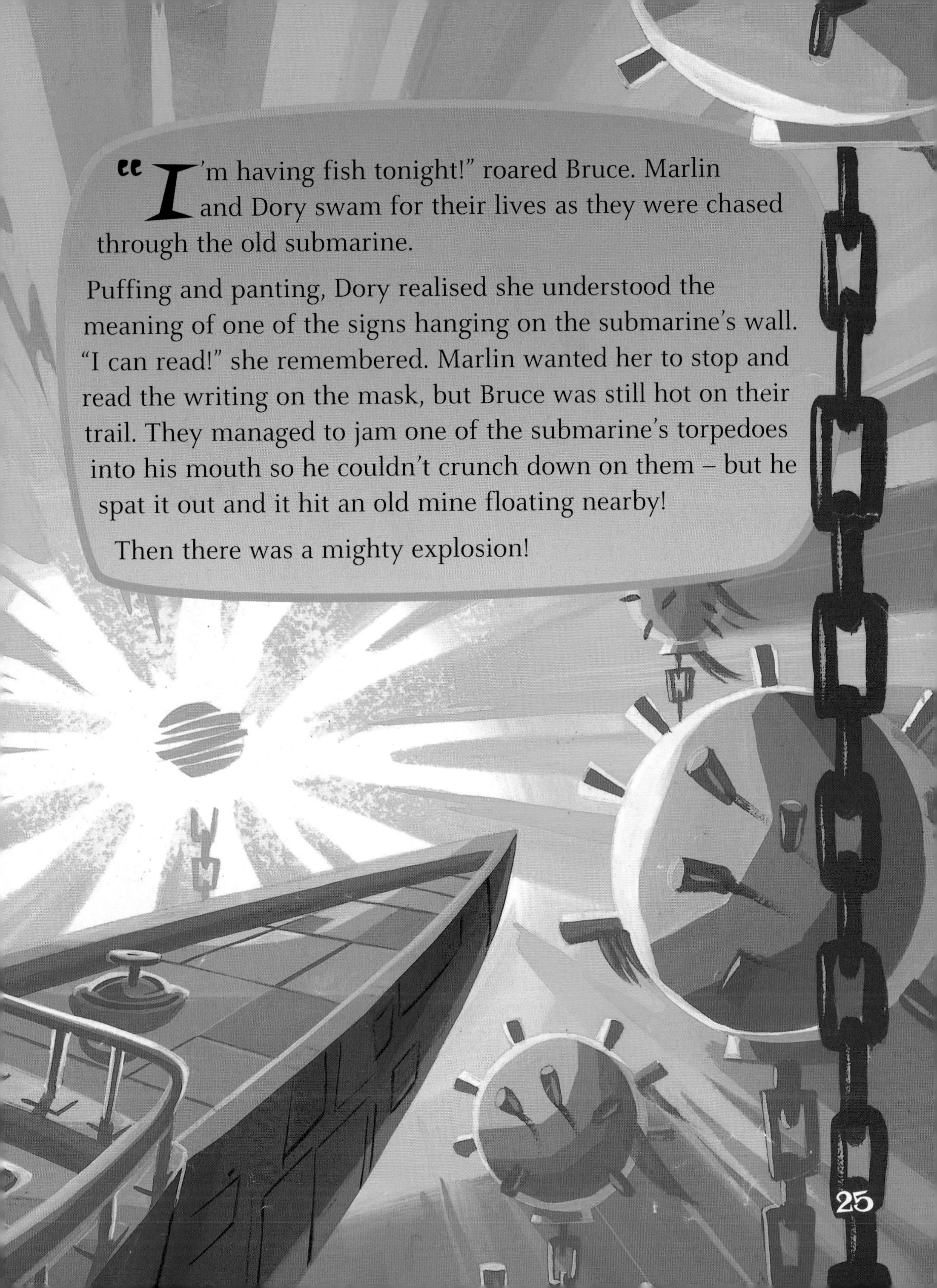

"I'm having fish tonight!" roared Bruce. Marlin and Dory swam for their lives as they were chased through the old submarine.

Puffing and panting, Dory realised she understood the meaning of one of the signs hanging on the submarine's wall. "I can read!" she remembered. Marlin wanted her to stop and read the writing on the mask, but Bruce was still hot on their trail. They managed to jam one of the submarine's torpedoes into his mouth so he couldn't crunch down on them – but he spat it out and it hit an old mine floating nearby!

Then there was a mighty explosion!

Meanwhile, thousands of miles away, Nemo found himself dropped with a plop into strange waters. He swam past all kinds of strange objects – even a plastic volcano – but kept bumping into walls he couldn't see.

Slowly, curious fishes of all shapes and sizes came out of hiding: Peach, Jacques, Bloat, Gurgle, Deb and her sister Flo (although Flo was really just Deb's own reflection). They were the Tank Gang, and explained to Nemo that his new home was in a fish tank in a dentist's surgery.

Nemo realised that the diver who grabbed him in the ocean must have been the dentist! "I want to go home!" he cried.

Before long, Nigel, a friendly pelican, landed on the window ledge to visit the Tank Gang. They had just introduced Nemo to Nigel when the dentist noticed the big bird and chased him away, knocking over a picture of a scary-looking girl. The dentist picked it up and looked into the tank. "Say hello to your new mummy," he smiled at Nemo. "Darla's going to be eight this week and you're her present!"

The Tank Gang were horrified to hear that Nemo would be soon given to the dentist's niece, Darla. She was known as the "fish-killer".

"I can't go with that girl. I have to get back to my dad!" cried Nemo.

Gill, the leader of the Tank Gang, introduced himself. Nemo was amazed to find Gill had a bad fin too – but he didn't seem to let it get in his way.

Later that night, the friends in the tank told Nemo he could join their gang, "If," Bloat whispered, "you are able to swim through THE RING OF FIRE!" It sounded scary, but really it was just a circle of air bubbles rising up from the plastic volcano.

To the gang's delight, Nemo swam through it with ease. Now Gill could share with him his plan to escape the tank.

Far away in the ocean, Marlin awoke to find the explosion had pushed them to the edge of a steep trench. When he woke Dory, she accidentally dropped the mask and it fell down and down and down. They swam after it into the darkest depths of the ocean. Suddenly, a single bright light came bobbing by – it was the glowing antenna of a hungry anglerfish!

The light it cast allowed Dory to read the writing on the scuba mask. "Speed read!" Marlin ordered, as he tried to keep the fish's light close by without being eaten alive.

"42 Wallaby Way, Sydney," Dory announced finally, as the anglerfish suddenly charged. Marlin trapped it with the mask, and he and Dory made their escape. They'd found an address – but could they find Nemo?

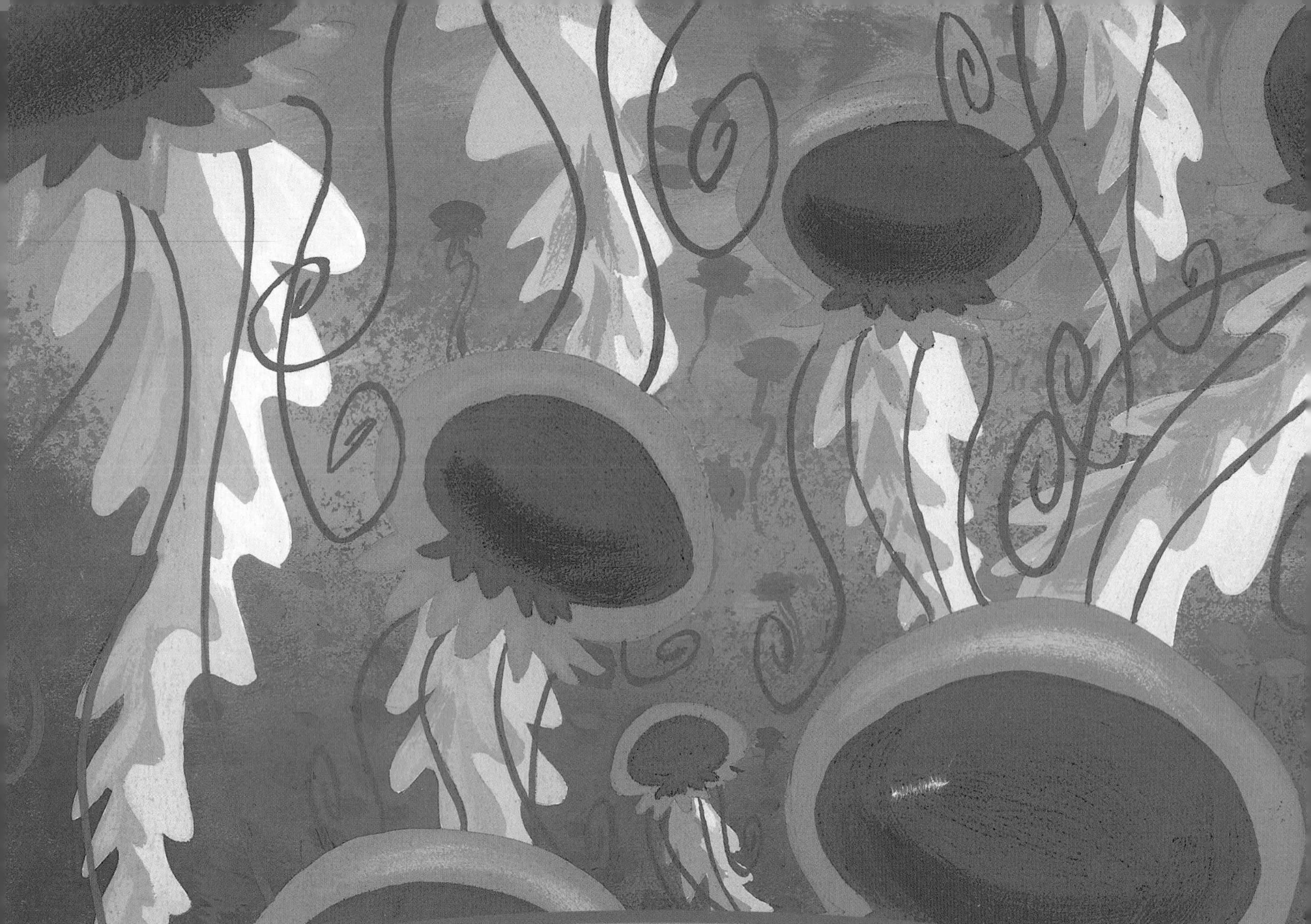

Dory asked some passing moonfish for directions to Sydney. They warned her to watch out for a big trench nearby, and that whatever happened, she should *not* swim over it. Unfortunately, Dory immediately forgot the advice and when they swam over the trench she and Marlin were surrounded by a forest of stinging jellyfish!

"All right, here's the game!" called Marlin, not wanting to scare Dory. "Whoever can hop the fastest out of here wins!" They bounced bravely from jellyfish to jellyfish, keeping clear of the stinging tentacles. Marlin was almost enjoying himself, until he looked back and saw Dory was in trouble. She was trapped and needed help.

Bravely he swam back to save her, dodging the stinging tentacles. Because he lived in an anemone, Marlin was immune to the small stings, but when he made it back with Dory he was weak and weary.

Back in the tank, Gill explained his escape plan. If they could block the cleaning filter, the dentist would have to clean the tank himself. He'd put the fish in bags of water, then they could roll out of the window and into the harbour below!

Everything depended on Nemo – the only fish small enough to do the job. "It'll be a piece of kelp," Gill told him.

Nervously, Nemo swam into the filter.

But something went wrong. The pebble he had managed to jam into the system came loose and Nemo found himself being dragged helplessly towards the filter's deadly blades!

"Stay calm kid!" Gill shouted. "Grab hold of this!" The tank fish grabbed a plant and helped Gill feed it through the narrow filter pipe. Nemo grabbed onto the plant with his mouth.

Finally – in the nick of time – the Gang pulled Nemo to safety. But the escape plan had failed, and Gill felt terrible that he had placed Nemo's life at risk.

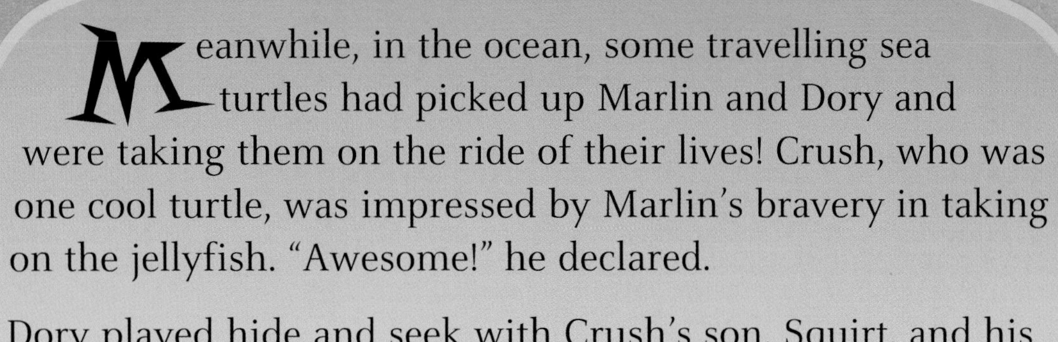

Meanwhile, in the ocean, some travelling sea turtles had picked up Marlin and Dory and were taking them on the ride of their lives! Crush, who was one cool turtle, was impressed by Marlin's bravery in taking on the jellyfish. "Awesome!" he declared.

Dory played hide and seek with Crush's son, Squirt, and his friends. Squirt did a lot of daring tricks but Crush didn't seem to mind. He trusted Squirt to know his limits. "How do you know when they're ready?" asked Marlin, amazed.

"When *they* know, *you'll* know," Crush replied.

Marlin couldn't help wondering if he'd been a little too protective of Nemo.

As Marlin swam closer to Sydney, he didn't know that tales of his adventures had spread far and wide. When the news reached Nigel he visited the Tank Gang at once.

"Your dad's been fightin' the entire ocean looking for you!" he told Nemo breathlessly.

The idea that his dad was battling his way to Sydney filled Nemo with pride – and new hope. Forgetting his fears, he swam determinedly back into the cleaning filter – and this time he *did* manage to jam it!

Nemo didn't know it, but his dad was now *very* close by! After saying goodbye to the sea turtles, he and Dory had accidentally hitched a ride in a *whale*. It took them all the way to Sydney Harbour before squirting them out of his blow hole!

"We made it!" Marlin cheered. "We're going to find my son! All we've got to do now is find the boat that took him!"

That was easier said than done. There were hundreds of boats in the harbour! They searched all night, but there was no sign of Nemo.

The next morning, Marlin and Dory were exhausted, but they continued the search until, suddenly, a big pelican flapped down and grabbed them right out of the water! Marlin and Dory wedged themselves in the bird's big beak. "I didn't come this far to be breakfast!" Marlin cried.

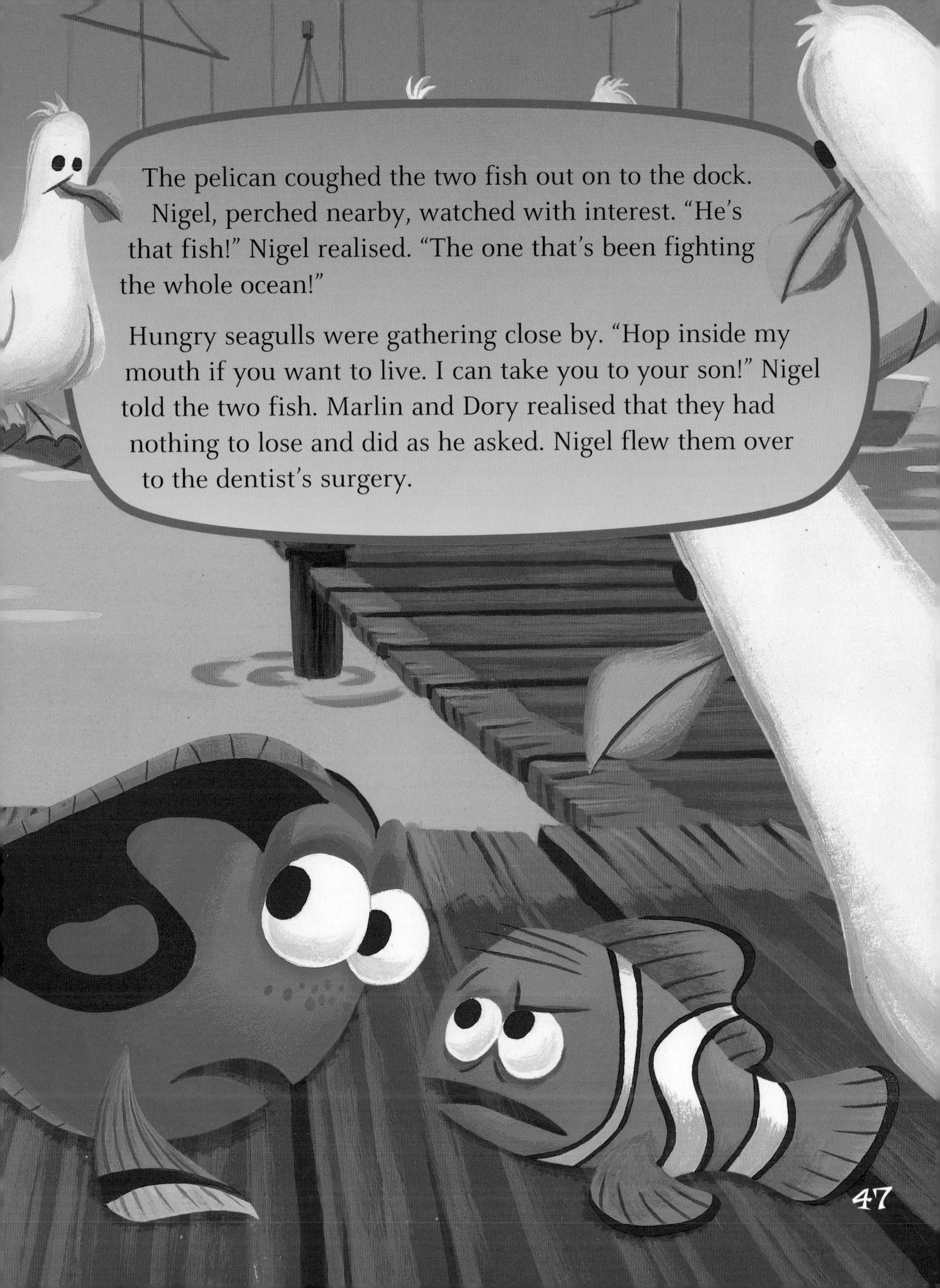

The pelican coughed the two fish out on to the dock. Nigel, perched nearby, watched with interest. "He's that fish!" Nigel realised. "The one that's been fighting the whole ocean!"

Hungry seagulls were gathering close by. "Hop inside my mouth if you want to live. I can take you to your son!" Nigel told the two fish. Marlin and Dory realised that they had nothing to lose and did as he asked. Nigel flew them over to the dentist's surgery.

Inside, the Tank Gang woke to find their water sparkling and clean! The dentist had got some kind of new high-tech filter! He hadn't even had to wake them up, let alone take them out of the tank! The escape plan had failed yet again.

"What do we do when the little brat gets here?" Bloat said, thinking of Darla.

"I'm thinking," snapped Gill. Just then, the dentist scooped Nemo up in a net and tried to lift him out of the tank. The others jumped in the net too and swam as hard as they could, making the dentist drop them. Nemo escaped, but swam right into a bag and was lifted out of the tank.

The doorbell rang. It was Darla. "Fishy! Fishy!" she demanded.

Nemo played dead, hoping the dentist would flush him down the toilet, since all drains led to the sea.

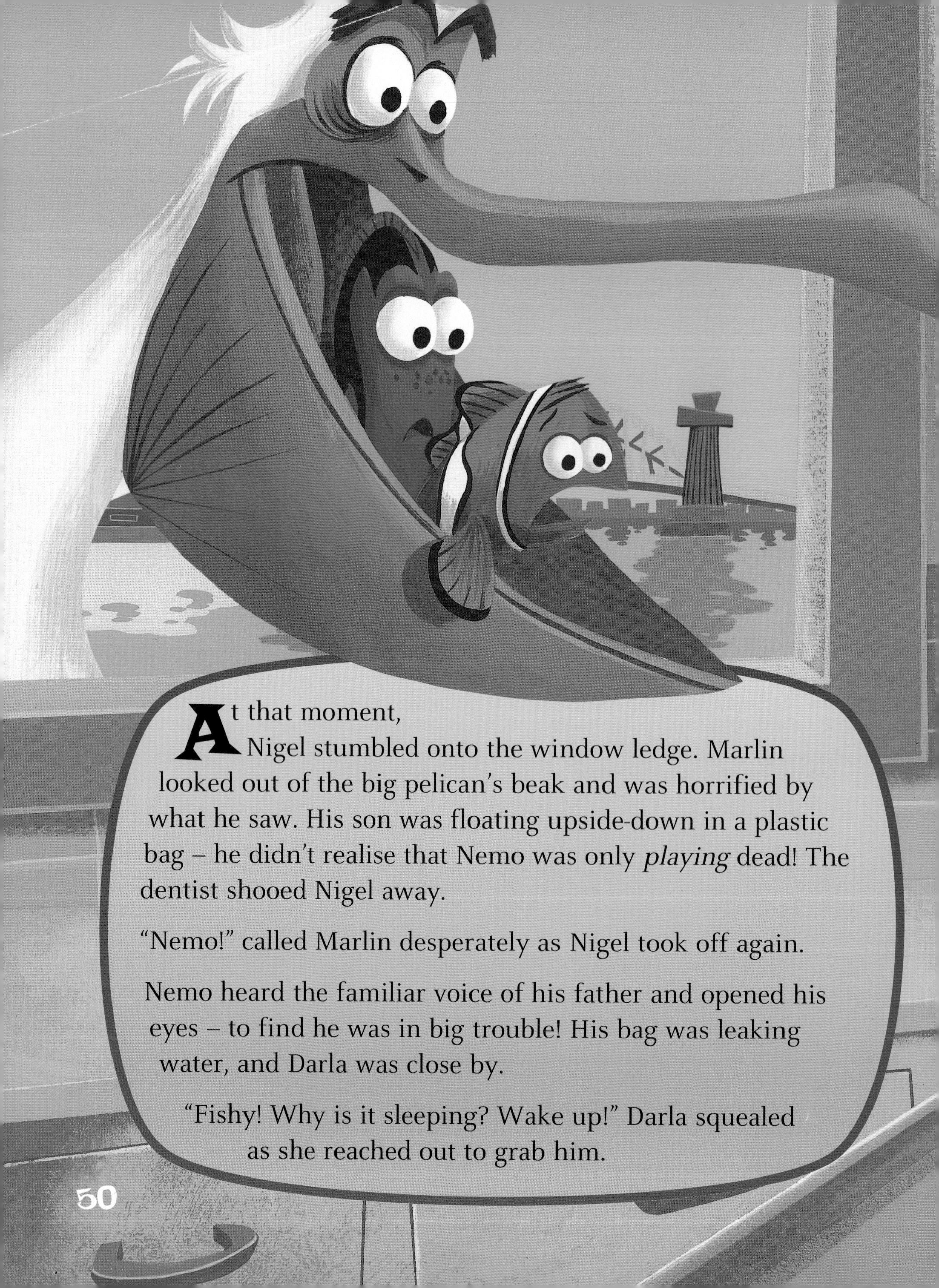

At that moment, Nigel stumbled onto the window ledge. Marlin looked out of the big pelican's beak and was horrified by what he saw. His son was floating upside-down in a plastic bag – he didn't realise that Nemo was only *playing* dead! The dentist shooed Nigel away.

"Nemo!" called Marlin desperately as Nigel took off again.

Nemo heard the familiar voice of his father and opened his eyes – to find he was in big trouble! His bag was leaking water, and Darla was close by.

"Fishy! Why is it sleeping? Wake up!" Darla squealed as she reached out to grab him.

"Hurry!" cried Peach, as the little clownfish splashed onto the dental tray. "Nemo can't breathe!"

"Ring of Fire!" yelled Gill, determined to save his little friend. The Tank Gang worked together to use the rush of bubbles from the volcano to launch Gill clear out of the tank!

Darla screamed as Gill landed on her head, bounced off again, and landed next to Nemo. "Tell your dad I said hi!" he yelled before managing to catapult a surprised Nemo right down the spit sink!

Meanwhile, Nigel sadly dropped Marlin and Dory back in the harbour. Marlin, who truly believed his son was dead, was broken-hearted. He needed to be alone, and told Dory it was time they went their separate ways.

“Please don’t go away,” Dory begged him. “I remember things better with you.” Marlin had become like family to her, and she didn’t want to be left on her own again.

“I’m sorry, Dory,” said Marlin. “But I *want* to forget.” With that, he swam away – alone.

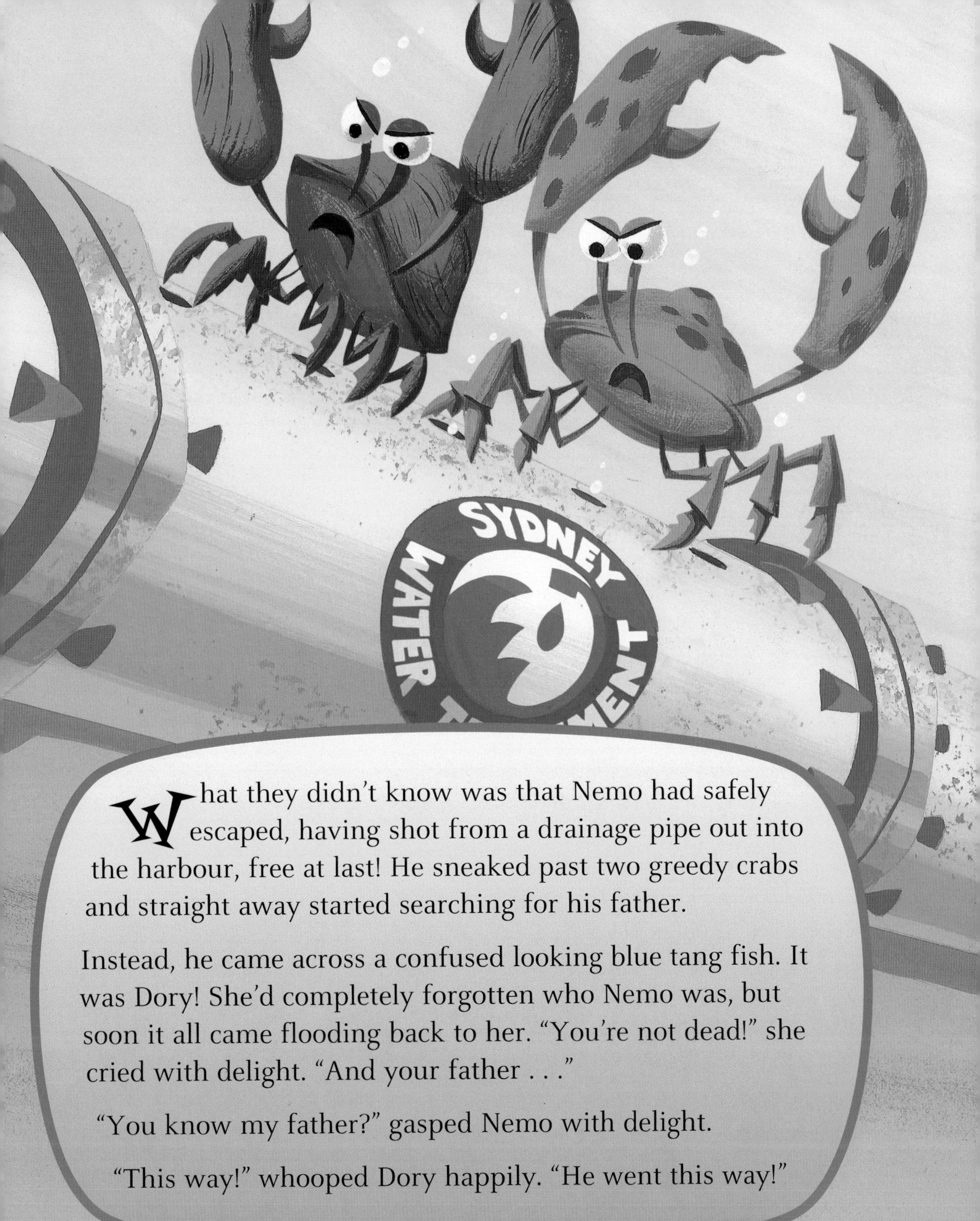

What they didn't know was that Nemo had safely escaped, having shot from a drainage pipe out into the harbour, free at last! He sneaked past two greedy crabs and straight away started searching for his father.

Instead, he came across a confused looking blue tang fish. It was Dory! She'd completely forgotten who Nemo was, but soon it all came flooding back to her. "You're not dead!" she cried with delight. "And your father . . ."

"You know my father?" gasped Nemo with delight.

"This way!" whooped Dory happily. "He went this way!"

Before long, they caught up with Marlin near a school of grouper fish. But before they could enjoy a reunion, a huge fishing net swept over the groupers and – disaster – Dory was caught too!

Nemo suddenly swam *into* the net! Marlin was horrified.

"We have to tell all the fish to swim downwards together!" Nemo cried. Marlin realised how brave his son had become.

Nemo's plan worked! The net broke, the fish were free, and Dory, Marlin and Nemo were finally all together at last!

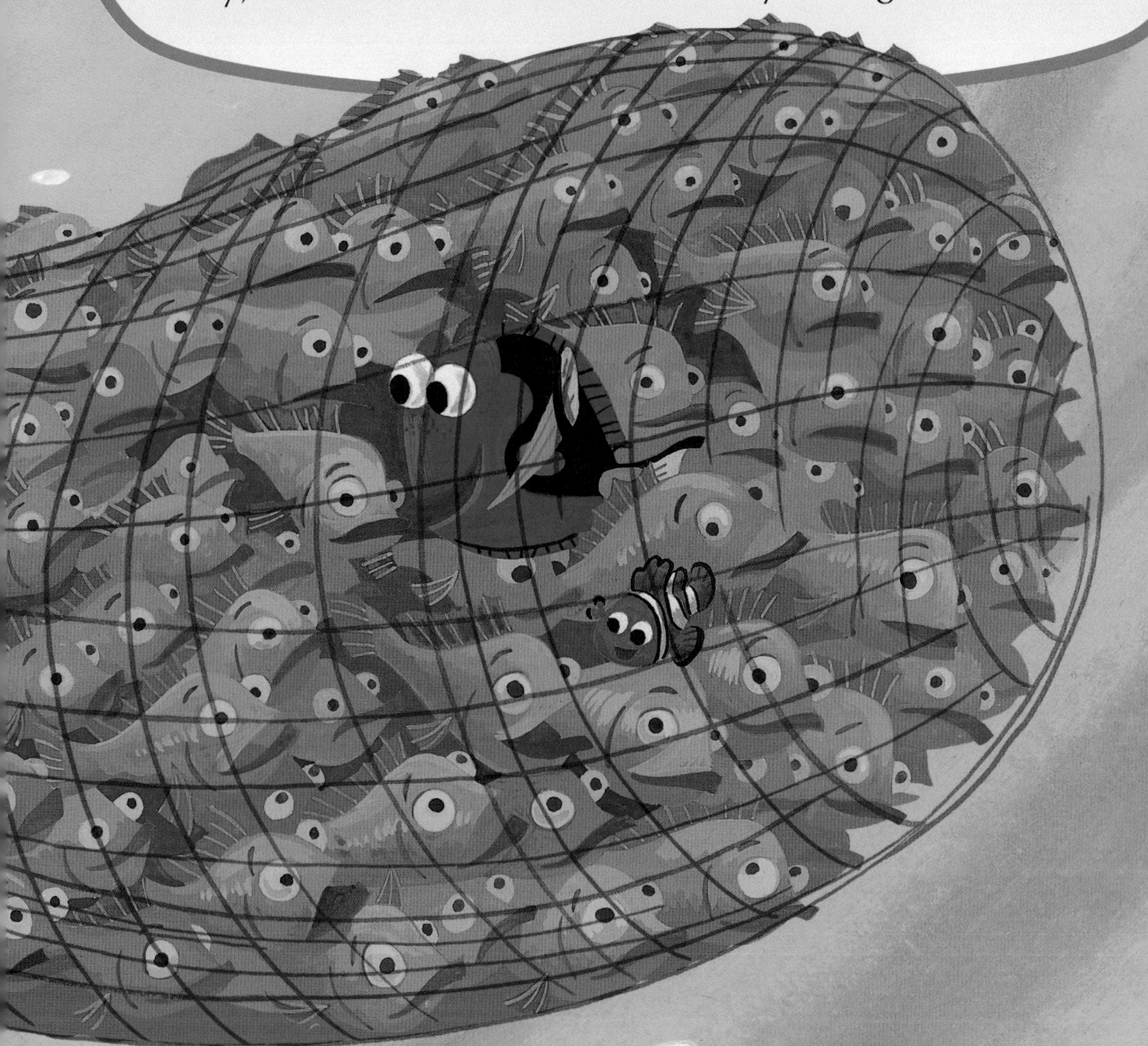

Marlin and Nemo made their way back home with lots of new friends and some amazing stories to tell.
Things were different now between father and son. Each morning before school they hugged each other, then Marlin happily waved goodbye as Nemo swam off with Mr Ray. "Now, go have an adventure," he said with a smile.

Far away, the Tank Gang was having an adventure too! They'd finally escaped by rolling into the harbour in little plastic bags. Now all they had to do was get out of them!